Butterflies, Boards, and Blessings

A Doctor's Journey to Thriving with Lupus

Dr. Manisha Rayavarapu (The Patient Doc)

Contents

Dedication

This book is dedicated to the warriors living with lupus and the family, friends, and caregivers that fight beside us. I truly hope my story will encourage and inspire you to not just survive, but thrive and live your best life.

Acknowledgements

I would like to acknowledge:

My amazing husband, Matthew D'Alessandro, who has been my rock throughout this battle with lupus. His continuous love and support are the reason I am able to live out my dreams.

My sweet baby boy, Micah, who has given new purpose to everything I do. He is my motivation to keep fighting and chasing my dreams, to never settle and never give up on my goals.

My parents, Joshua and Kalpalata Rayavarapu, who have taught me to always trust in the Lord. They have led by example, and their unrelenting love and faith has shaped the person I am today.

My sisters, Manjusha Birje and Meenakshi Rayavarapu, who are my truest friends. They've comforted me when

I'm hurt, corrected me when I'm wrong, and celebrated me when I'm successful. I can't imagine anyone else I'd want to go through the ups and downs of life with.

My best friend, Helena Khaleel, who is my sister from another mister. She is the one person I can always count on to have my back and be there when I need them.

My friends who have supported and encouraged me through my journey. Each one of you has touched my life in a special way and contributed to my story.

My Rheumatologists Dr. Marder and Dr. Carter, whose compassion and dedication have kept me healthy for the past ten years.

My coach, Dr. Jessie Benson, who has given me the confidence to be vulnerable and honest. Without her, this book would still be a manuscript on my computer.

My writing team, Dr. Shola Ezeokoli and Dr. Otito Okpor for helping bring my dream of publishing a book to realization.

Endorsement

I absolutely loved this book. I read it all in one sitting. I laughed and I cried. It spoke to my heart.

As a physician who has been living and thriving with lupus for nearly 40 years, it's not often I meet someone whose experiences, feelings, thoughts and wrestlings echo mine so closely. I felt like Dr. Rayavarapu had been reading my thoughts or reading my diary.

As both a physician and a patient, her poignant perspectives give us much to ponder and consider in this strange world called life with lupus.

The struggles are real, and understanding of what is really going on from an insider's view will make all the difference.

This is a fantastic book for people who have had lupus for a long time or just a short while. It's also a great read for those who care for lupus patients or who know and love someone living with lupus.

Dr. Manisha truly is the Patient Doctor. I am grateful that she so honestly shared her story and her heart. In these pages, we all can find inspiration.

Phyllis Nsiah-Kumi, MD, MPH
Internal Medicine and Public Health

Introduction

was diagnosed with lupus in May 2010, at the glorious age of 28. At the time, I was a second year family medicine resident working crazy hours, just trying to survive my final years of training. I was overworked and overstressed, underprepared and under rested. The conditions were perfect for lupus to make it's grand entrance.

The first few years were the hardest. My emotions ranged from confused to enraged to downright hopeless. To cope with my volatile emotions, I created an anonymous blog- a place for me to vent and commune with others living with the same disease. As my disease stabilized, and my blog gained traction, I realized I had a rare opportunity to create something good out of my unfortunate diagnosis. I could use my blog to help others, and bridge the gap between patients and doctors.

I started blogging regularly by sharing my journey,

discussing topics about lupus, and giving an inside look into the doctor world. My writing was inspiring others, and I felt moved to write a book sharing my story. I had always dreamed of publishing a book, and now knew what I needed to write about. Between managing my disease, working full time, and life in general, I became too busy, and gradually gave up blogging. If I couldn't even scribble a short blog post, how would I compose a full-length memoir?

It took several years, but finally my dream of publishing a memoir has come to realization. These pages tell the story of my life as a doctor living with lupus. It details the impact of lupus on my life, not just physically, but emotionally, spiritually, mentally, and sexually. I share my secrets to encourage others living with chronic disease that they can still live fruitful, satisfying, and happy lives. I also designed this book to raise awareness in those not living with chronic illness and provide a candid view into life with a chronic disease. I pray this book will bring hope to those living with a chronic disease, and a deeper understanding to those around us.

Chapter

1

How Could I Not Know?

"It doesn't look good" my supervising attending whispered gently as she looked over my test results. I had been rotating through the clinic that afternoon seeing patients when my primary care doctor called. I stepped outside into the quiet parking lot, hoping for some privacy and fresh air. He said it appeared something rheumatologic like lupus, was going on and he would fax my results to me. He gave me the number of a good rheumatologist he knew and wished me well. I snuck back in and retrieved the fax to show my clinic supervisor. She didn't need to say a word. Her distressed face told me everything. Shocked and in utter disbelief,

I asked to be excused early from the clinic and raced to the only place I knew I could be alone; the call room's fire escape, a.k.a, the hospital's unofficial smoking section.

I sat there, in the dusty stairwell, for what seemed like forever, staring at the two pieces of paper that would change my life as I knew it. I desperately struggled to make sense of it all. In addition to the test results being unfamiliar, it also seemed impossible that something like this could be happening to me. I pleaded with God, praying this wasn't real. With tears streaming down my face, I reflected on all the things I had been feeling for the past year. How could I not know?

I had been feeling unusually tired with occasional random knee or wrist pains, but I was a medical resident who worked sixty hours a week, ran up and down stairs, and wrote endless orders and notes. I was always on overnight calls completely discombobulating my sleep cycle. It was not unreasonable that my knees and wrists hurt. The exhaustion was expected. My hair had started falling out and clogging the drain, but I was incredibly stressed with exams and PowerPoint presentations. This was just part of being a resident, right?

It was vanity that had led me to the doctor. I had just returned from vacationing in California with my boyfriend. The flight had arrived late, and since he lived closer to the hospital, I stayed the night at his apartment with him and his beautiful fluffball Persian cat, Stitch, who I was highly allergic to. I awakened the next morning to puffy eyes and a bloated face. I looked hideous and felt embarrassed for anyone to see me that way. I took some anti-histamines and figured it would just get better. It didn't. Instead, my cheeks were so swollen, I could barely see out of the slits that were my eyes. This definitely needed to be addressed.

Due to my inability to see, my boyfriend drove me to a doctor that we found at the last minute on Google. The older Russian doctor was friendly and surprisingly thorough for a simple allergic reaction; conducting a complete review of systems and exam, in addition to ordering urine and blood tests. He didn't tell me why, and I just figured he was doing a complete physical since this was my first visit. I was sent home with a few days' worth of steroids and my symptoms resolved in due time. I did not think much about the tests until I received that phone call.

But here in the stairwell, it all started to come together. There was a reason for all the things I had been experiencing. I wasn't lazy; I was just very fatigued. I realized my symptoms had been showing up long before this year. Since childhood, I would always get red, itchy, painful rashes on my arms and face—that textbook butterfly rash across my nose and cheeks—when I went out in the sun. Those odd aches and pains that could never really be explained but were often rationalized as exercise-related soreness. I had been wearing wrist braces at night for what I thought was carpal tunnel syndrome. I spent hours doing "surgery" on my ingrown toenails because I thought they were the source of toe pain. I never checked the pads of my toes to see the tiny red spots indicating inflammation in the blood vessels.

The stress and excitement of the California road trip with my new boyfriend just triggered a flare of the insidious disease that had always been there. During the journey, the pain in my right knee had gotten worse. I hobbled around in a soft knee brace as we visited wineries in Napa and went sightseeing through Fisherman's Wharf in San Francisco. I remember limping on a wine tour, lagging far behind older couples in their sixties. I was embarrassed, so my boyfriend jokingly told everyone I had a rugby injury. By the time we had finished visiting sharks and jellies at the Monterey Aquarium and made our way to our final destination, I was depleted.

Here I was with a whole itinerary of things to do on our last night of vacation in the City of Angels and I had no energy. Like our gas tank, I was running on empty. All we could do was hunker down in the hotel room and order Mexican food for dinner.

Two weeks later, I found myself driving an hour's distance to a large teaching hospital in Long Island to meet my rheumatologist. I walked through the halls with my stomach churning. So, this was what it felt like to stand on the other side of the front desk. Sitting in the waiting room I felt anxious and mostly unprepared. This was unlike me. I was usually over-prepared for most things but here I was—speechless, unsure of what to say or what to ask—something this talkative girl is usually not.

Thankfully, the empathetic rheumatologist knew exactly what to say. She spoke confidently with a calmness that was reassuring. This kind-faced doctor listened patiently to me explain my symptoms before she began conducting a complete exam. She skillfully palpated my skin with her warm hands, checked my mouth for sores, listened to my heart and lungs, and manipulated every joint in my body. She tentatively diagnosed me with lupus but stated I would need to do more bloodwork.

She suggested a kidney biopsy to assess for damage but wanted to wait until my labs came back. After prescribing an increased dose of steroids, she went over a provisional treatment plan, and scheduled me for a follow-up visit.

Fourteen tubes of blood and a couple of weeks later, I was back in her office. The blood work confirmed her diagnosis. I, indeed, had lupus, but thankfully, my kidneys were still healthy. The early start of steroids by my primary care doctor had helped prevent damage. We discussed my treatment plan, and she prescribed a new medication to help with symptoms. Follow-up appointments and blood work would become a monthly affair. There would be other specialists to see along the way, including an ophthalmologist because the new medication I was on could cause increased pressure in my eyes. It was a lot to take in during this visit, but I felt safe and in good hands.

In addition to new medicines, I would need a new lifestyle. I would have to find ways to reduce stress in my life and get more rest; something nearly impossible for a resident. This meant cutting out socializing on free weekends to catch up on much needed sleep. I had to quit smoking (Yes, doctors make unhealthy life choices too) and stop taking oral contraceptive pills due to the risk of clotting. I would need to modify my diet and eat less inflammatory foods. That meant more vegetables, less red meat, less fried foods and, and little to no alcohol intake. Up until then, my idea of vegetables were onion rings and French fries. To my dismay, this also meant that I would have to pass up on favorite Carnival day meals at the hospital cafeteria.

Although it was a relief to finally have a diagnosis, the realization that I had lupus terrified me. I remembered being in medical school, studying immunology and rheumatology, reading about lupus and multiple sclerosis, and thinking those were the most horrible diseases you could get. There was no cure, just medical management. These people suffered, became disabled and were generally debilitated by their disease. There seemed to be no hope.

My visit to an educational meeting on lupus only confirmed my feelings of despair. I had driven excitedly into the city for the first time since I was diagnosed. I was going to a meeting filled with people like me, to learn more about our disease and resources available to us. I don't know what exactly I was expecting, but this was far from it. The meeting hall was a wide and welcoming conference room in a nice hotel. What surprised me was walking into a room full of older people, or perhaps they only appeared older due to the toll the disease had taken on them. People who appeared in their forties walked in with canes, skin damaged and scarred, their exhausted faces looking like they had been awake for days. And maybe they had. God knows, between the anxiety and pain, I wasn't sleeping much either.

People were scattered among the rows of chairs, and I chose a seat near the back in case I needed to make a quick escape. I sat quietly and listened as speakers walked up to the microphone one at a time, spoke matter-of-factly, and returned solemnly to their seats. Much of what they explained was information I already knew. I wanted something more, but what did I want? Did I expect them to say it would all be OK, that lupus really wasn't that bad, that they had discovered some new miracle drug? The meeting ended with a question and answer session, which turned into conversations about how to get Medicaid and resources for disability and government assistance. I left the meeting feeling unsatisfied and fearful. Is this what life was going to be like for me too?

I didn't give up on my optimism completely. I went

to another meeting. This time a small support group. I went with the intention of at least making some new friends who would understand everything I was going through. But I had nothing in common with the participants. Most of them were at home all day, unable to work due to disability. I wanted to be around people who were thriving with the disease, working their forty hour weeks, going on vacations, and living life to the fullest. I wanted to know and see that I could have a normal life. With this group, I had nothing in common except this miserable disease.

They do say, "third time's the charm". I tried again but this time to a " Lupus Young Leaders" meeting. Here were young ladies who were thriving. They had jobs, wore fashionable clothes, and strutted with confidence. They were living with lupus and maintaining normal lives, even socializing after work. These were the people I aspired to be like. The only problem was they all worked together and had formed their own little clique. I'm sure I could've squeezed in and become part of their little band if I tried. But, between work and feeling drained all the time, it was impossible to make it out to their social gatherings in the city.

After that, I decided to stop focusing on lupus.

Obviously, it was not going to go away, but I just diverted my energy to surviving and completing my final year of residency. From that point on, I would keep the reality of my disease tucked away and pretend it didn't exist.

Chapter

2

The Invisible Disease

There are four different types of lupus, but the one I was diagnosed with is called systemic lupus erythematosus (SLE), which is the most common and affects 1.5 million people in the U.S. alone. Lupus mostly affects women and is more common in women of ethnic descent. It is an autoimmune disease that can attack any and every organ of the body. A normal immune system exists to fight bad bacteria and viruses and prevent them from infecting the body, but in autoimmune diseases, the body creates autoantibodies that attack normal body tissues. The most common organs affected are the joints, skin, kidneys, and lungs. Lupus has inactive periods, where life can be almost normal. Then there are active periods called flares, where everything goes bananas.

I've had my fair share of flares, usually during or following a period of intense stress. That first flare that led to my formal diagnosis was awful, but it was not my worst.

A couple of times since then, I have had episodes of severe pain involving my entire body. One time I had a stomach virus and had been having diarrhea and vomiting all night long. I woke up the next morning with immense pain searing through every joint and muscle. It is hard to describe, but even the slightest movement or gentlest touch had me crying in agony. My boyfriend struggled unsuccessfully to change me out of my pajamas and into regular clothes that I could wear to the hospital. We were forced to settle on his baggy sweatpants and an over-sized T-shirt. Even the soft fabric rubbing against my skin caused me discomfort.

He drove to the hospital at an unearthly speed, pulling over once so I could vomit by the side of the road. We pulled up to the emergency room entrance where he ensured a speedy hand-over to a nurse who wheeled me back immediately. As I lay on the cold hospital bed giving my history to the doctor, I wondered if I sounded like a drug seeker to him. So many times I had attended to patients who came to the ER moaning and groaning in pain. In many of these instances, we labeled them as drug addicts trying to get more opioids and a quick high in the ER.

They gave me morphine which only made me sleepy and did not even come close to relieving my agony. I suffered in pain until my bloodwork came back and it was deemed safe to administer an intravenous non-steroidal anti-inflammatory medication (NSAID). The ER doctor admitted me for further evaluation and started intravenous steroids. This was the first time that I was admitted into a hospital, and unfortunately, it wouldn't be the last. The silver lining that day was that with my weakened immune system, I had to be given a private room. The medications did their magic, and I was out within a couple of days with a new prescription for prednisone and a recommendation to follow up with my doctor.

A few years later, I was working full time in a busy medical clinic operated by a non-physician administrator who cared more about numbers than patients or employees. I was overwhelmed in my attempts to provide the best care for my low income, noncompliant patients while still meeting my assigned metrics. My commute was forty-five minutes each way in heavy traffic. I was desperately trying to lose the weight that I had gained due to the steroids, so I would come home and work out strenuously. In addition to all of that, my boyfriend was working very long hours as a surgery resident, which meant we were struggling to make time for each other. Talk about the perfect formula for another flare.

This time I had serositis, specifically pleuritis. Serositis is inflammation of the serous membranes (lining of an organ), such as the pleura (lungs), pericardium (heart), and the peritoneum (abdomen). So that meant I had inflammation of the lining around my lungs. I experienced pleuritic chest pain- a sharp, catching pain whenever I took a deep breath. I also felt shortness of breath and a heavy sensation in my chest like weights in my lungs.

I remember being at work, moving quickly between rooms, barely able to catch my breath. The sharp pain would make me wince while talking to my patients. I remember feeling so winded that all I desperately wanted was to just sit down. It was however impossible, what with a fully booked schedule and unexpected walk-ins. For weeks, I pushed myself, worked hard and hid my symptoms from my colleagues. I did not want my task-master employer to find out and somehow use it against me. No one had any idea about the battle I faced every day.

I didn't realize at first that my chest pain was related to lupus. I thought I had bronchitis. But when it got worse, and the chest decongestants were not helping, I called my rheumatologist. She immediately ordered a CAT scan to verify that I did not have a pulmonary embolism (blood clot in my lungs). When that came back negative, she ordered an electrocardiogram (EKG) and echocardiogram (ECG) to confirm there was nothing wrong with my heart. After those were ruled out, she diagnosed me with pleuritis and started me on a prescription non-steroidal anti-inflammatory drug (NSAID).

The medication helped with the pleuritis symptoms but caused problems of their own. For the first couple of hours after taking the medication, I would be in this drowsy state where it felt like I was outside of my body watching myself interact with my patients. It took me twice as long to type out my notes after patient encounters. I fought hard to stay awake and focused. Thankfully, once the symptoms started to resolve, we were able to switch to more tolerable medications.

Lupus is also associated with other conditions. I have Raynaud's disease, which is a condition in which the arteries of the fingers and toes constrict when exposed to cold or stress. I can't even reach into the freezer without my fingers burning and turning blue. This condition is not usually dangerous, but it can lead to ulcers and gangrene. I had a young patient once with lupus who had lost a couple of fingertips due to tissue damage.

I also have anti-phospholipid antibodies. This means I am at risk of developing blood clots (deep vein thrombosis) in my legs which could then travel to my lungs (pulmonary embolism). What is even more worrisome to me is that it can cause miscarriages (spontaneous abortions). In addition to taking low-dose aspirin daily, I make it a point to keep active and drink enough fluids to prevent clotting.

I would also from time to time, experience what is known as "lupus fog". My mind would feel cloudy and I would have trouble concentrating. Sometimes I would lose track of what I was talking about. Occasionally I would forget words and have trouble expressing myself. It would seem as if I was distracted or spacing out. It didn't happen often or last for long, but I always feared it would affect my ability to practice medicine.

Lupies, as some in the lupus community call themselves, can also develop lupus nephritis, which is when lupus attacks the kidneys and causes irreversible kidney damage. Patients sometimes require dialysis for end-stage renal disease and kidney failure is the leading cause of lupus-related death. Although I never had nephritis, I still have this fear of someday developing it.

I could go on about all the other diseases related to lupus, but then I would have to write another book. Lupus has the potential to affect every organ in the body. I've experienced symptoms related to my gastrointestinal tract (reflux) and blood vessels (vasculitis) and skin (sun sensitivity and the classic malar butterfly rash). People with lupus are also prone to other autoimmune and connective tissue diseases such as, but not limited to, scleroderma, ulcerative colitis, and Sjogren's disease. The complications and symptoms are endless.

Because of the involvement of multiple organ systems, lupus is often a delayed diagnosis. Often patients will have very vague symptoms, such as fatigue and achiness. Sometimes the symptoms mimic another unrelated disease, causing a misdiagnosis. If you have ever watched the medical drama "House," you may recall lupus is always one of the suspected diagnoses. Other

times, patients will have multiple symptoms, or vary-
ing symptoms, which can cause patients to be labeled
as hypochondriacs or attention-seeking. It can be very
frustrating, and patients can suffer for years before an
actual diagnosis is made.

Lupus is often called an invisible disease because
people with lupus can usually look healthy and normal,
even when they are extremely sick. It's not like cancer,
where patients can become very thin and frail, and lose
their hair from treatments. We do not have any physical deformity or apparent symptoms like coughing or
wheezing. Apart from the time just before diagnosis, I
had never looked ill. Before steroids, I looked like my
normal self. After steroids, it just looked like I had
gained a lot of weight. Nothing about my physical appearance indicated that body was secretly at war with
itself.

This was a double-edged sword . On one hand, it
meant I could easily hide my ailment. It was simple
to keep my secret from people whom I felt would judge
me. I had a lot of pride in myself and my work and
was embarrassed by my disease. I felt ashamed of the
limitations it caused me and did not want anyone, especially my current and future employers, to think I was

disabled. It also made it easier for me to lie to myself and pretend that I was normal. The downside was that those whom I did want to know that I was sick, did not believe me.

Chapter

3

Why Don't They Understand?

was finishing up my second year of residency, ready for my third and final year, when I got my diagnosis. I had been preparing to become a co-chief resident with a good friend of mine, but my diagnosis threw a wrench into that plan. The position of co-chief was now out of the question as I would not have the extra time or energy to manage resident schedules and assign calls and patient-presentations. Although I had plenty on my plate with managing this disease, and I couldn't take on any extra responsibilities, I did not feel that I needed to leave residency.

Surprisingly, not everyone felt the same. I had told my program director, and the other residents in the program assuming other physicians would understand the most, but that was not the case. I had expected empathy, but that was not what I received. Imagine my astonishment when my good friend, who would become chief, demanded that I should take a medical leave of absence as she believed I might become a liability. There were three levels in the hospital and getting to the different floors involved running up the stairs because the old, rickety elevators were too slow. She argued that I would not be able to make it to the hospital floor in time to run codes on critical patients. She and some of the other residents also worried I would not be able to handle the workload and that they would have to carry the extra weight. I felt betrayed, but I understood why they felt that way.

During our second year, one of the residents in our class became pregnant. She had horrible morning sickness and would come in to work ninety minutes late, which meant missing the most important part of the day: "Morning Report" which was when we received updates from the on-call team about what happened overnight. We would discuss patients' emergencies or status changes, and if any new patients had been added to our list. The attending physicians would then go over the plans for each patient for that day. After that, we went to the floors to see our assigned patients with an attending physician who would tell us what orders to write, what labs to keep an eye on, or what procedures to prepare for. If you weren't there in the morning, then you would have no idea what was going on with your patients. So, someone else from the team would have to take notes and evaluate patients for the absent colleague, in addition to managing their own. I must admit that I used to feel a little annoyed about the situation at the time. Looking back, I wish I would have shown more empathy and understanding.

Leaving residency was out of the question for me. I knew that if I took a leave of absence, it would be difficult to return. Fours year of college plus four years of medical school meant eight years of debt that would be impossible to pay back. Even if I took a research position, I was not likely to make enough to pay back my student loans. I had no choice but to complete my residency so I could start paying off that mountainous loan and all the accumulating interest. I also needed to stay to keep my sanity. Working afforded my life a degree of much needed normalcy. If I kept busy, I would not be able to focus on my disease and any of the fears I had about my future. I begged the program director to let me stay. Thankfully, he showed some compassion and allowed me to remain in residency.

The third year of residency had a lighter workload, with less time spent on overnight calls and less time running around seeing patients on the floor. The interns and second year residents did most of that. My program director adjusted my schedule with easier electives and more clinic time to enable me to finish out most of my final year without much stress. I had already done more than enough ward rotations to meet my requirements. My clinic supervisor was accommodating and would let me leave a little early to make it to doctor appointments. The only issue was my overnight calls. My colleagues rallied for me, and each one, except for the unsympathetic co-chief to be, covered a night for me. In the end, I only needed to complete one of my calls.

My work colleagues were not the only physicians who didn't understand. My closest friend prior to my diagnosis was a dermatology resident at a hospital near mine. We became fast friends after meeting in medical school. She was a generous host and fabulous cook, so another close friend and I would always meet up at her place to study. During the week, we would watch Grey's Anatomy together in her cozy apartment, anticipating what residency would be like for us. On the weekends we would go out dancing or socializing at a bar. She loved to party, and I always had the best times with her. She convinced me to do clinical rotations with her in New York, where she was from. When I moved to New York for residency, she took me under her wing and introduced me to all the trendy restaurants and bars. When we just wanted a quiet night in, she'd invite me over for a scrumptious meal and girl talk. Every time we got on the phone to catch up, we would end up chatting for over an hour, swapping crazy residency stories, or whining about clueless men.

Everything changed after I developed lupus. I could no longer go bar-hopping or stay out all night. I needed my precious sleep to be able to function. Despite knowing about my diagnosis, she still made a big deal if I did not want to come out to the city with her. I would come sometimes to appease her, and if I decided to leave early, she'd be vexed. I attempted to explain to her that I was exhausted and hurting, but she never understood.

When we wanted to meet up for dinner, I would invite her to come over to my apartment instead. I could order delivery and we could catch up and watch a movie. She always insisted I drive the forty-five minutes to her, where I'd circle around another twenty minutes just to find a parking spot a five-minute walk away. But, I no longer had that kind of energy.

We had planned a trip out of town to attend another friend's wedding and booked a hotel room together. After I got sick, I was terrified to travel, especially without my boyfriend, the only person who knew exactly what I was going through. She became angry when I canceled, even though I offered to pay my half of the room charges. I still came, but with my boyfriend, and we didn't stay the night, which frustrated her further. She blamed my lack of desire to hang out with her on my new boyfriend, often complaining that I only wanted to spend time with him. She felt I was choosing him over her, breaking the girl code.

She never saw the real picture where I was dying to go out like I used to. I missed dancing and listening to live music. I was desperate to be independent and free-spirited again. She was the one person I could always talk to about anything, but I could not talk to her about the most important issue in my life.

I gave up on a lot of friendships after that and lost all motivation to make new friends. I felt envious of my friends and their apparent freedom. I would have good days and bad days. People assumed that since I seemed fine one day, I was fine every day. I always felt they thought I was making things up and exaggerating my illness. I got frustrated with the snide comments about how nice it must be for me to be able to only work part-time. I grew weary of explaining to people who didn't take any interest in learning about lupus, why I could no longer do certain things. This lupus, wasn't just some disease I had, it was a huge part of me. If you couldn't understand what lupus was, then you couldn't under-stand me.

My parents, the biggest supporters in my life, didn't understand either. But it was not their fault. They lived in Florida, and I lived in New York, so they weren't around to see what was happening to me and I inten-tionally kept it that way. They would ask to come visit when I was in the hospital, but I didn't want them to see me suffering. There was nothing they could do to help, and I didn't want them to be worried all the time. I avoided flying back home and often minimized my symptoms when talking to them on the phone. They knew I had lupus but didn't know much about it other than it was a rheumatologic disease. My mother blamed herself, thinking it was something she gave me, despite my reassuring her it wasn't so. They wanted to understand but it was just so complicated. While I knew I always had their love and prayers, they however, had no idea what was really going on with me.

I felt very isolated and lonely during this time, and still do. I went from being the center of attention to an outsider. I was like a social outcast who didn't fit in with normal, healthy people. Luckily, I had some friends in residency who were still there for me and a best friend back home who was only a phone call away. And of course, there was my godsend of a boyfriend.

Chapter

4

A Love Story

met my now-husband during residency training. He
was part of the batch of new interns who started
during my second year. Since he was a surgery tracked
resident spending his initial rotations on the surgical
service, I did not get to meet him for a few months. I had
heard the surgery team had one male intern, but I had
no idea who he was.

Inevitably, I ran into him while on call doing an admission in the ER. As second year family medicine residents, we were responsible for running codes, so I could
not disappear even for a minute. Since the hospital's
cafeteria closed at five, I would usually ask an intern

to pick up some tea and snacks for me from the Dunkin Donuts across the street. Most interns happily obliged, as it allowed them to vacate the hospital for a breather and also grab something for themselves.

Not him. The second the words left my mouth, he blankly replied with a "No." He would rather stay and work than take a quick break. I was speechless. Who did he think he was? I couldn't believe he was refusing my request. I was, after all, his senior. No other intern, or student, had ever said no. I wanted nothing to do with this unsociable character.

I did not encounter him again until after Thanksgiving. That night, I was on call for medicine service and he was on call for surgery. All of the overnight residents had met briefly to place orders for food, and he was responsible for collecting our monies and paying the delivery guy. I did not have the money on me, so he kindly offered to cover me. Perhaps he was not as frosty as I thought.

I finally got a chance to pay him back a couple of days later and we started making small talk. He let it slip that he had an Xbox. Now, this was a gamechanger for me. I had just played this crazy zombie killing game over Thanksgiving break, and loved it, but did not have an Xbox of my own. As luck would have it, he not only had the Xbox, he also had this exact video game! I politely invited myself over on the weekend, to which he surprisingly agreed.

I went over knowing full well that I was using him to get another chance to play video games. I walked shamelessly into his apartment and found him in the kitchen where he was cooking up a storm. Portions of ravioli were boiling in a pot and he was frying up juicy meatballs. I wasn't anticipating this. This was not a date, and I had never had a guy cook for me. Honestly, I never cooked for me either, so this was quite an unexpected treat. That night we connected over Italian food and 'massacring the undead' on his Xbox.

Our friendship blossomed after that. He was incredibly easy to talk to: a quiet, shy man, who only spoke when necessary. A perfect listener for a chatterbox like me. We'd talk about work and joke about oddball attending physicians and interesting patient stories. He had a dark and sarcastic sense of humor. Every time we conversed; I would end up in stitches from laughing so hard.

His friend told me that he was interested in me, but he never made a move. I was preoccupied with fawning over an orthopedic intern I had casually been seeing to be bothered. Despite my lack of interest, we still hung out frequently as friends, and talked on the phone almost every night. One Saturday night, we both were craving steaks, so we decided to treat ourselves. We deserved it, after a hard week at work. We went to a fancy steakhouse that he used to frequent with his father. He brought out this eighty dollar bottle of wine, which was surprising for someone on a intern's salary. When the bill came, he graciously paid. I offered, but he would not even let me contribute. I didn't want him to think that this was a date and I proceeded to tell him that I didn't have any romantic feelings toward him, and only wanted us to be friends.

But, somewhere along the way, things evolved. I found out the orthopedic resident was also seeing someone else, and it broke my heart. I knew the relationship wasn't serious, but I was still crushed. My friend was there for me, listening to me cry and vent for hours at night. He would make me laugh so I could forget about my so called rejection. He'd invite me over or take me out to keep me from wallowing in self-pity. I had loved the bad boys, but maybe it was time to love a good guy. His friend had been trying to convince me to give him a chance, and maybe it was time. After all, they say "best friends make the best lovers."

It is hard to describe the transition in our relationship because it felt as if nothing had changed. We were still best friends who cared deeply for one other. We still chatted on the phone for hours and hung out any chance we got. We still shared secrets and talked about everything with each other. The only difference was that our conversations became more serious as we contemplated plans for the future.

We had planned a best friends road trip to explore California, where he grew up. After our relationship status changed, we turned the trip into a romantic adventure, adding Napa to the itinerary. Instead of cheap hotels and fast food, it became bed-and-breakfasts and candlelit dinners. Slowing down and getting away from the madness at work exposed feelings I did not realize I had. We embraced every shared moment on that trip, in spite of my newly developing symptoms. Every experience felt heightened simply because we were together. It felt completely natural to convert our friendship from being best friends to being a couple.

Unfortunately, that "honeymoon" ended quickly, and reality kicked in as I became sick. Really sick. We went from eating eggs at brunch to discussing freezing my eggs for the future. If my kidneys were damaged, I'd have to be placed on a medication that could kill all my eggs. Talking about having children felt too serious a conversation for two people who had only begun dating a month ago.

My boyfriend had now assumed the role of caregiver. He would bring me dinner, cook for me, and help me tidy up. I struggled to do simple things like brush my hair due to pain in my wrists, and he would have to help comb out my tangled mane. I would often wake up multiple times in the middle of the night, and he would have to assist me in getting out of my bed to use the bathroom or give me more pain medication. Eventually, the going back and forth from my place to his became too cumbersome, and we moved in together just four months after we started dating.

He even had to help me one night at work. I still had that one overnight call I had to take. I had been working since seven in the morning. It was now three in the morning of the next day, and I was feeling drained. I had a patient in the ER who would need admission orders but was still getting pre-admission work done. It was going to be a straightforward consult, but I did not want to wait around for the patient to be ready. I went upstairs to the call room to get a little shut-eye before my pager went off. I woke up at six a.m. terrified that I had not heard my beeper go off. When I called the ER to find out what had happened to the patient, I discovered that my boyfriend had done the consult on my behalf and left the it for me to sign-off on.

I finally started getting better after the steroids kicked in but that didn't mean it was back to being rainbows and unicorns. The steroids made me very agitated; I became impatient and snarky and would snap at him for the littlest things. I spoke words that I could never take back. I said things that were hard to forget, things that I can still see reflected in our relationship. My appearance also changed: The steroids had caused my body to expand, and I went from being in shape to looking like a shapeless blob. I was not the same independent and fearless person that he had fallen in love with when we had started dating. Even so, he still stayed.

Eventually, I was weaned off the steroids and started becoming my normal self again. I was more happy, less snappy. I was able to take over household duties again and take responsibility for more chores. His residency was getting busier, and I was able to care for him. I would bring him dinner at work when he was on call or grab some food for him when he was stuck in the operating room during lunch. I planned activities and adventures where we could bond and discover new things together. The roles reversed a little and our relationship started to balance out.

We dated for three years before we got married. I did have my concerns. We loved each other, but we were very different people who wanted different things out in life. I thrived in social atmospheres and struggled with his homebody nature. He, on the other hand, was a workaholic, often taking on extra work, instead of coming home to spend time with me. I wanted to move back to Florida, buy a home, and start a family; he wanted to pursue further training and have the option to travel to higher-paying locations for work. I was sick of living in New York, dealing with crazy traffic and icy winters that took a toll on my body, but he loved the frosty weather and busy city life. Several times I considered leaving and starting a new life back home, but I always stayed.

He had his own concerns with marrying me as well. He had ambitious goals for his life, for work and for leisure, which he feared I would hinder due to my health. He had always believed that it was important to pass on his genetic material and have children of his own. He was apprehensive that I would not be able to have children due to complications from lupus. He also worried I would become sicker as I grew older and he would be unable to take care of me because of the demands of his dream career. His greatest fear of all was that I would die and leave him all alone.

Another thing we both were unsure of was our intentions for marriage. We both knew we loved each other but were we contemplating taking this next step for that reason alone? I feared he was staying with me out of guilt. I knew he had felt guilty about staying with me so long and not making the commitment I had been waiting for. He would have felt unsettled leaving a sick girl. I agonized that I was only marrying him because I did not think anyone else could love me.

By God's grace, we were able to look beyond our fears and doubts. But the battle was far from over. His father and step-mother were against us getting married. They were initially unaware that I had lupus since I kept my diagnosis hidden for fear of judgment. After Hurricane Sandy hit, we were unable to live in our little bungalow due to lack of electricity and proper sewage and we had to move in with them for three weeks. I still had to go to work, but my commute was now an hour and a half each way, and I would come home sapped to the point where I couldn't do anything in the house, even on my days off. When the aftermath of a severe snowstorm caused a gas shortage, people had to stand in long lines in freezing temperatures to fill up fuel cans at the gas station. My boyfriend had to be the one putting gas in my car because of my inability to tolerate the cold due to Raynaud's disease. My future in-laws assumed I was lazy and was only using my boyfriend for an easy life.

The entire period of our engagement was a miserable back and forth battle with them, and we eventually had to tell them about the lupus. As expected, the news elicited the same concerns that my now-husband had. His father wanted grandchildren and was unsure that I could fulfill that desire. He wanted his son to marry a young healthy woman, who would both be able to take care of him as well as his future family. I felt they wanted someone who could cook and clean, and be the perfect Susie homemaker, all while holding down a power job. I suppose I could understand that, but should people with chronic diseases never get married? Did my disease negate all the good in me?

We came very close to calling off our wedding, but my fiancé and I were undeterred. After premarital counseling, we got married but not quite as planned. We had slated our wedding for Labor Day weekend but I would be leaving my job at end of July, which meant two months of no medical insurance; a big no-no for me. We ended up getting married earlier, at the beginning of March, at our church away from church since our planned wedding was to have been at my previous church in Florida. We needed a couple of witnesses for this new arrangement, so a good friend and her husband met us at the church. As fate would have it, the pianist was there practicing for service and offered to play "Here Comes the Bride" for us. It was the cutest impromptu wedding, and we still had that September wedding at my home church followed by a wild reception at the zoo, where we fed giraffes and took pictures on a carousel.

We have had our fair share of trials throughout the years. We have struggled to find balance in our marriage as our roles shifted. We have both made compromises because of our jobs and my disease. We have faced immense uncertainty and fear of the future. At times, it's been an uphill battle, but we've climbed together, and for that, we are stronger. Our love story may not have been a fairytale, but I believe it was part of God's narrative. After all, my husband's name means "Gift from God."

5

Side Effects

We often talk about how a disease affects us, however, a big part of what people with chronic illnesses feel is due to the side effects of their treatments. The life-altering medications prescribed for me improved my health, but also transformed my appearance and personality. I changed so drastically, I barely recognized who I was anymore.

After years of self-loathing from middle school through medical school, I had finally started liking my body. I had joined an awesome women-only gym close to home where I felt comfortable exercising without judgment. I had even hired a personal trainer. The pounds were dropping, and I was beginning to see definition in my muscles.

Then I started high-dose steroids, and became a hungry, hungry hippo who couldn't stop eating and snacking. Maybe it was a bit of depression as well, but at meals, I would eat to the point of engorgement. For some reason, the steroids made everything taste good to me, even foods I was previously averse to. I knew weight gain was a side effect of steroids, but I didn't see any changes initially, so I thought maybe they wouldn't affect me that way. Then, I woke up one morning and it seemed as if I was twenty pounds heavier and squishy all over. I developed the characteristic "buffalo hump" and rounded face caused by steroid use. I had fluid retention which only added to the weight gain and appearance of heaviness. One time I had so much swelling from my feet all the way up to my thighs that my relaxed fit jeans turned into jeggings. My legs felt like I had put exercise weights on them.

My long, shiny, dark hair, my singular pride and joy, had thinned out severely and lost its luster. I had to cut it into shortened layers to give it some volume. My soft skin became so dry and patchy that no moisturizer could help it. My usually dewy face developed dark patches that I had to conceal with makeup. No amount of contour could disguise the puffiness of my face.

I was disgusted in my appearance and felt ugly and unattractive. This was a level of insecurity far worse than what I had felt in high school or college. I could not stand my boyfriend touching me because I thought was hideous, and I didn't think he wanted to touch me either. I was nothing close to the cute, bubbly girl that he was dating a couple of months ago. I stopped making the effort to look good. I used to love dressing up, coordinating jewelry and accessories, matching my makeup to my outfits. Now I could barely be bothered. I hated how I looked, and my self-esteem plunged deep into a dark pit.

It became impossible to keep up with the whirlwind of my emotions. Think PMS multiplied by ten, but lasting for months instead of a week. My familiar friend, prednisone, was to blame for this. One minute I was sad and crying for no apparent reason, the next I was perky and peppy. I would be like an irate bee ready to sting anyone in her presence, then sweet as honey dripping from the comb. In addition to the depression and emotional lability, the prednisone caused me to have constant anxiety. I had always been a bit of a worrywart, but now I was anxious all the time and would frequently have minor panic attacks. I was riding an emotional rollercoaster, knocking out anyone in my path.

My energy levels fluctuated constantly as well. Some days I would be jittery and raring to go. I would have so much drive and focus, with enough stamina to feel like I could conquer the world. Nothing could stop me on days like these. It was like I had one too many cups of espresso. I would overdo it and crash. Hard. Then, I'd barely be able to move, straining just to open my eyes or even get out of bed. Other days I would have insomnia and find myself awake until the wee hours of the morning contemplating the most random things. Thankfully, we were able to remedy that by splitting up my dose of steroids. I would take a larger dose in the morning and a smaller one at night, but I still could not get a good night's sleep.

Then there was my Benlysta®. My inflammatory markers had been creeping up and my rheumatologist suggested that I start this medication before I had another flare. I had felt fine and did not want to add another medication to the list, especially one that would be given by intravenous infusion. I had read horrible stories on different online forums about severe headaches and nausea due to this drug. I didn't see the need to fix what was not broken.

My doctor was right, I did have another flare, and had to start taking the medication. Because it would take time to get authorization, and since the medication would not start working right away, I had to restart the steroids. Once the authorization came through, every four weeks I had to drive one hour each way to get poked multiple times with a needle as they searched for a vein to infuse the drug. Did I mention that I am afraid of needles? The aspirin and prednisone caused me to bruise easily and my arms looked like I had been physically abused. It was embarrassing to wear a short sleeve shirt without a cardigan. I did not get any nausea or headaches with Benlysta® but I experienced extreme fatigue and a weird feverish sensation that would keep me glued to bed for the rest of the day.

Another just as worrisome but overlooked "side effect", that was not spoken of was the cost of the drug. The infusions cost a few thousand dollars a month and required prior authorization. My insurance covered it, but I still had to shell out a co-pay of two hundred dollars. I was able to get co-pay assistance, but I knew many other patients who were not able to. I also had to deal with calling the insurance company and the mail order specialty pharmacy multiple times a month to ensure due coverage and prompt shipping of the medication. Every month it was the same hassle of being bounced around on the phone, unsure if my medication would arrive on time for my appointment at the infusion center. It would not be easy to reschedule an appointment which could end up delaying treatment and causing me symptoms until I received my next dose. It is a terrifying feeling wondering if you will be able to get your lifesaving medication for the month.

Chapter

6

Fear

had grown up very sheltered with parents who were always afraid to let us do many things. They were scared to let us near the stove or use anything sharper than a butter knife; scared to let us date because we would get pregnant or become distracted from our studies. They feared letting us go out with our friends by ourselves because we would be kidnapped; feared letting us drive because we might get into car accidents. My life was based on a lot of fears and restrictions, so when I finally had my freedom, I threw caution to the wind.

While away at college, I proceeded to do anything I wanted without fear of consequence. I will admit some of the things I did were somewhat risky, but I was living life, exploring, and taking chances. I loved new experiences, especially if it involved traveling or meeting people.

My favorite adventure was when I went road tripping through California for residency interviews by myself. My parents had accompanied me to college and medical school interviews, and when they offered to accompany me for my residency interviews, I declined. I wanted to do this on my own. I had lined up three interviews in different cities that were miles apart from each other. I knew I would never accept a residency so far away from family but I just wanted the opportunity to travel. I flew out to LA, borrowed a cousin's car, and took to the highway. I made it to two of my interviews before my dormant free spirit awakened and I went off course. I skipped the last interview to cruise the beautiful Pacific Coast Highway and go sightseeing. As I pulled onto a bluff and looked over the edge at sea lions sunbathing on the beach, I felt this exhilarating sense of freedom and independence that I had never felt before.

Lupus changed EVERYTHING.

I underwent a rapid 180 degree turn from fearless to fearful. I used to travel back home to Florida every three months to visit my family, but now stopped going as often. I was terrified to be on an airplane by myself. I imagined having some acute incident like a stroke while I was airborne, and not being able to get to a hospital in time. I worried I would have a flare while I was at my parents' house and they would have no idea how to take care of me. They had never seen me sick, or exhausted or in pain. I was always considered the strongest one of my sisters, and I feared how they would react to my new illness. When I would visit, before I got sick, I would usually go out and try to meet up with friends. After I got sick, I limited my visits to my one best friend who also was a doctor. She was the only one who understood.

I became inappropriately dependent on my boyfriend as he was the only one who knew me and my medical history. Even when I was feeling well, I found myself clinging to him like Saran Wrap. I panicked at the thought of being alone; never knowing what could happen to me. I would wait for him to come home from work, all while feeling helpless and lonely. I was scared to drive by myself, especially at night. I never wanted him to leave or go out with friends. I became so accustomed to him doing simple things for me, that I would still ask him for help even after I became fully capable.

He was now a caregiver instead of my boyfriend. My fear and insecurity had created an unhealthy dynamic in our relationship.

The limitations from my disease had made me lose my passion for travel. What was the point? I could no longer do the things I loved. I would not be able to keep up on guided nature trails, especially if there was any uneven terrain. I would be in too much pain to go sightseeing and walking through a city. Forget the beach. Even lying out in the sun would cause my skin to break out in a rash. I would have no energy left at the end of the day for a romantic dinner. Foreign locations were out of the question because I would be at risk of contracting some dangerous disease because of my low white blood count. I did not want to book tours or make reservations because I always felt there would be some reason related to my health that would cause me to cancel at the last minute.

The fear consumed me and filled every part of my life. I was like

a skittish scaredy-cat; a powerless little girl with no control over her life. Everything was centered on fear and the reasons, or more accurately the excuses, I had made for myself. I could not do the things I wanted to not because of lupus, but because of my anxiety. The bondage of fear had tied me down. It was not a disease disabling me; it was fear.

There comes a point though, when the fear becomes too much to hold on to. Like a lump of burning hot coal, or a heavy rock, you need to let it go. I tried all sorts of things to manage my fears, but only one thing brought me peace. The remedy for my fear was faith.

Chapter

7

Faith

I was raised as a Seventh-day Adventist (SDA), a Christian who observes a Saturday Sabbath, believes in the Trinity and awaits the second coming of Christ. Throughout the years, my feelings toward Adventism and religion, in general, has fluctuated. I've explored other religions and faiths, but no matter where I went, I always returned to my Adventist roots.

Growing up, I didn't really like being SDA. I mean, what kid likes getting up early on a Saturday morning to sit through a long church service instead of watching Saturday morning cartoons? Friday sunset to Saturday sunset was our Sabbath and day of rest. No secular activities were permitted: no watching TV, no going to the mall, and no swimming in our pool. We could not even do boring homework. The only thing I was allowed to do was go to church, and if I was lucky, eat lunch at a church-friend's house after the service. I usually resorted to napping, after the Sabbath meal, to pass the time. I would restlessly count down the minutes until sundown on Saturday night, while formulating plans for the evening.

It seemed as though my whole life revolved around being SDA. Even my education. In the beginning of third grade, we moved from Maryland where I had attended public school to a small town in Florida. From then until tenth grade, I attended the church affiliated K-10 school. It was a huge change for me, and I missed my old school.

Our new school was really small, with seven to eight kids in a grade, and two grades combined in most classrooms. I was teased a lot, mostly because my school was predominantly white, and the students had never been exposed to Indian culture but also because I was eager to learn and asked a lot of questions. My school in Maryland had been very diverse, and it was common to have friends of all ethnicities. I had never been ashamed of the fact that we smelled like curry until we moved to Florida. In Maryland, I had been admitted into a program for gifted children at school, where the students were just as inquisitive as I was, but here students were annoyed at me for raising my hand. I missed my gifted program, and wished they had something like that for me here. My chicken-loving self also hated the no meat policy at school. Since Adventists were mostly vegetarian, we were only allowed to have vegan meat substitutes for lunch.

I basically existed in a little bubble with the same circle of friends from church whom I attended school with. I knew every student in every class from kindergarten through tenth grade, as well as their parents. Every social or extracurricular activity was with the same group of people and their families. We even had our own boy/girl scout-like program called Pathfinders and we went on camping trips and conferences with other Pathfinders in the country. As a child, I was content with this, but as I moved into my teenage years I started to feel more out of place. It was a really nice school, and the teachers genuinely cared about their students, but I wanted more.

We did not have much contact with public school kids, except for the couple who attended church but were not enrolled in our school. I grew up believing that they were bad kids and that public schools were full of drugs and sex. In spite of this, I was sometimes envious of them; they could wear whatever they wanted to school, while we had such strict dress codes. There was no expression through clothing at my school; No jewelry, sleeveless tees, or skirt hems above the knee were allowed. I had considered going to public school for my final years of high school but wanted to be able to graduate with my current classmates.

When it came time for my last two years of high school, I followed suit and attended an Adventist boarding school that was three hours away from home. It was a lonely time for me and I missed my family and my mother's cooking. It was a co-ed school with separate boys' and girls' dormitories. We were allowed to mingle outside the dorms all day but once the clock struck eight at night it was back to the dorms for lockdown. We had no TV and had to use payphones in a hallway to call our families and friends. There was no privacy. On Saturday mornings we had to "check-in" at church unless we were sick. If we wanted to go out for the weekend, a parent or an approved parent of a friend had to sign us out. Forget about prom and homecoming dances. We weren't supposed to dance because it was considered too sensual, so we had boring meatless banquets instead. It all felt so restrictive. I had watched shows, like "Saved by the Bell," or "Boy Meets Girl," and dreamed of what it would be like at a normal school. Therefore, when it was time for college, I opted for a non-Adventist one.

In college, even with my newly found freedom, I continued to attend an SDA church but mostly out of a sense of obligation and maybe guilt. I was just going through the motions because it was all I had known my whole life. It was not that I did not believe in God anymore. I still did, and I still wanted to feel close to God. I joined a nondenominational youth group and attended their meetings and social outings regularly. I prayed when I remembered and tried to keep up with a daily devotional. I had moments when I felt close to God like He was right there with me, moments when I felt committed to my childhood beliefs, but those were few and far between. I still had faith, but it was weak. I was more focused on other things.

I was overwhelmed with grueling biomedical classes and late-night study sessions. I was meeting new, interesting people- people I could be myself around. My world was opened to things I had never seen or done before in my little Adventist school world. I tried at first to keep the Sabbath, but it got very lonely being the only one in my dorm room on Friday nights, while all my roommates were out at parties or clubs. Eventually, I gave in and started going out to bars and clubs. I would return early in the morning after a night of dancing, my hair stinking of smoke. I would roll out of bed a few hours later, with barely enough energy to shower, and make it to church just in time to hear the closing hymn. I was doing things that I knew I shouldn't, and I did not want to face God out of embarrassment and rebelliousness. I was subconsciously, or maybe consciously, distancing myself from God. I only prayed as a last resort when I needed something. God had taken a backseat in my life.

I was essentially treating God as my genie; God, please help me pass this test; Jesus, please take my pain away; Lord, please make my ex-boyfriend love me again. Even with the best intentions, my prayers became Santa's wish-list. I would pray constantly for things I wanted but most times it felt as if my prayers fell on deaf ears.

I was always bargaining with God, it seemed; If You do this for me, I promise I will make it to church on time; If You answer this prayer, I will stop smoking; If You give me this one thing, I promise to lead a life more dedicated to You. If my prayers were answered, I would keep my promises for a little while. Once I was no longer in need I would revert to my usual ways. I continued a pathetic cycle of only returning to Him when I needed something.

My prayers and pleas only ramped up when I was diagnosed with lupus. I would beg to be healed, but I still struggled. "Why was this happening to me?" "What did I do to deserve this?" I became angry with God, furious that I was trusting Him, but I was still suffering. I thought that God did not care for me, or that He simply did not exist. I turned to other sources for comfort or answers. I felt foolish for believing in Him and I turned my back on Him. But God was still reaching out to me.

It took me many years before I realized I had been praying for the wrong things. I was asking Him for what I wanted, but never did I think to ask what He wanted for my life. I realized that most of things I had prayed for in my life, no matter how good or right they seemed, were not always the best for me. With hindsight, I started to notice how different situations could have unfolded if my plans had come to fruition. I decided to start praying for God's will, instead of mine, to be done in my life.

This required some faith, especially for a control freak like me. Faith is more than merely believing in God's existence. It's letting go completely and letting God steer the ship. It's trusting him in every moment of your life. Trusting him with not just the big decisions, but the small ones too. Not just when things were going bad, but also during the good times.

I struggled with the idea of letting someone else be in control of my life. Sure, I could make my own decisions, but I needed to follow God's lead—even when it did not make sense to me. I am a methodical person; I need things to be logical. I would analyze situations, see no solution, and become hopeless. I would lose faith easily, letting fear overwhelm me. I would forget to trust God and His perfect plan. Sometimes, if I simply did not like the direction things were going, or if the solution was taking too long, I would become impatient and would slip back to doing things my way. My stubborn nature constantly instigated mental standoffs with God.

Eventually, I learned to release my obsession with being in control of everything, and peace came. I love a particular biblical phrase taken from Philippians 4:7 KJV- "the peace which passeth all understanding." It tells of a peace greater than I can comprehend, a peace that comes even when I do not understand what is happening. This is the kind of peace I experience with God. I realize there will be pain and suffering sometimes, but I have the peace of knowing that no matter what happens in my life, God will see me through it. My favorite story in the Bible is that of Joseph, the boy with a coat of many colors. Just like He did with Joseph, God carefully set everything in motion to lead me to where I am today. When I am afraid or anxious, I cling to the Bible verses and stories I learned in my childhood and I feel calm. Peace replaces my fear and anxiety and creates room for joy and gratitude to move in.

And I have so much to be thankful for. I am thankful for my supportive friends and loving family. I am thankful that with God's guidance, I chose a husband who was perfect for me, a very caring and patient man.

I am thankful that despite having lupus, I can still work and function from day to day. I am thankful for my struggles—as cliché as that sounds—they have made me a stronger person and drawn me closer to God. I am thankful for my parents who raised me on a Christian foundation that I can stand firmly on when the ground feels shaky. Although I took it for granted at the time, I am thankful that I was able to attend Christian schools where my teachers cared not only about my academic future, but also my spiritual one. And despite my resistance, I am thankful that God guided me throughout the arduous journey of becoming a doctor.

8

About That Doctor Thing

From the day I was born, I was predetermined or perhaps predestined to become a doctor. The announcement donuts frosted with pink icing might as well have read "It's a doctor" instead of "It's a girl." My sweet little baby-self didn't know it then, but everyone else around me knew.

Growing up in an Indian family, I had only three career choices: a doctor, a lawyer, or an engineer. My parents aspired for me to become a doctor because they had both desired to go to medical school as young adults living in India but were unable to do so because of financial and family circumstances. They both had become nurses instead and wanted more for me. As I got older, they considered my studying law because of my natural affinity for arguing but decided medicine would be the more honorable choice.

As a young child, this was something I was quite proud of. When people asked what I wanted to be when I grew up, I confidently replied " I want to be a doctor". Everyone at my church, my schoolteachers, and friends knew that I was going to be a doctor. All my cousins, my aunts, and my uncles knew I was going to be a doctor. I was already a doctor in the making. My life was set; there was no other path for me.

I worked diligently toward that goal, mostly at my parents' prodding. I studied hard, especially in science-related courses. If it was not an A, it was not good enough. Even an A minus would not cut it for my parents. I participated in both band and choir so I would be considered well-rounded. I took piano, voice and flute lessons. I had preferred to be in the percussion section of school band, but my parents thought the flute would be more fitting for a girl and so flute it was. I volunteered for food drives and soup kitchens at the church. I visited patients in nursing homes and volunteered at the hospital. I even took a job serving food to residents in an assisted living facility—anything to strengthen my college and medical school applications.

Another thing I did to boost my application was to shadow a doctor who owned his own concierge practice. This was where my doubts about becoming a doctor started to creep in. The doctor I shadowed was very pleasant but the work itself seemed very boring. He was very caring with his patients, but the time spent talking with them was a lot less than I imagined it would be. A lot of time was instead spent on documentation and paperwork, and this was before electronic health records were made mandatory. He talked a lot about insurance companies; how they were not letting doctors be paid what they were worth, and how they were charging patients more than they should. He had opened his concierge practice so he could have more autonomy and keep the money he earned. Although he hadn't been in practice too long, he was already starting to get jaded.

Regardless of my uncertainty, I stayed on track as this was the only thing I knew. I never seriously considered other professions. Honestly, I didn't know much about any other professions that were out there.

My childhood dream had always been to be a famous rock/pop singer and actress. I joined the drama team and always starred in school plays. Deep down I felt I was destined for the big screen. I was passionate about writing poetry and composing songs. I had a notebook full of poems and song lyrics that I had written but kept to myself. One of my most memorable nights in college was when I read one of my original poems out loud at an open mic night as a random band of guys played instruments behind me. In that sacred moment, I felt complete.

But a dream is still just a dream. Millions try to make their dreams come true and fail. What would make me the one? Although I felt like was unique—maybe even special—I had the sense to know all of this was just a pipe dream. I already had something I excelled at. I knew I could succeed as a doctor. Therefore, I made the practical and reliable choice.

After my first year of college, I started to realize medicine was not for me. I was doing well in all my classes—getting straight A's, but something just didn't feel right. Up until then, I had not given serious thought to what I really wanted in life. Then, my first boyfriend came along. He opened my eyes to a world of possibilities I never imagined. He gave me a certain confidence in myself that I had never experienced. I did not have to be perfect; with him, I was enough as I was. I finally felt comfortable in my own skin. He showed me that I was my own person who was allowed her own intelligent thoughts and ideas. My first love broke barriers and my heart in just a matter of months.

I was now at a college where people studied to become anything they wanted to be. They were taking classes to be marine biologists, criminal investigators, and music teachers. The opportunities were endless. In my first semester, I took a human behavior class which intrigued me, and I considered switching my major from biomedical sciences to psychology. When I told my parents about this they were unsurprisingly furious. They threatened to pull me out of the university and send me to community college because they felt my indecision was serving to waste time and money. I didn't want to leave my new friends or give up my freedom, so I conceded.

I dragged my feet in applying to medical school. By the spring semester of my senior year I had still not applied to medical schools or taken my medical college admission test (MCAT). All of my medical school-bound colleagues had taken their MCAT in the spring of their Junior year and had applied to their favorite medical schools that fall. The application window had closed, and I figured I would just take a gap year, work, and see how things went. I was already working at the college as a research assistant in the neuroanatomy department. Maybe I could just increase my hours there?

All was going as I planned until my parents heard of a new medical school forty-five minutes away from home that was considering applications past the standard deadline. Begrudgingly, I applied just to appease them, knowing there was no way I would get in without an MCAT, which I was not scheduled to take until May. I sent in my application, took my test, and celebrated graduating college and having a whole year to "discover" myself.

The admissions board must have seen something intriguing on my application because they offered me an interview without receiving my MCAT score. I interviewed well, and they told me they were interested in me, but could not decide without my MCAT scores. A few weeks later I received a letter stating they had already filled their seats but would put me on a waiting list in the event of another candidate having a change of heart.

This is what I had expected and had even counted on: I was free, or so I thought.

A couple of weeks later, while vacationing with a previous college roommate in Wisconsin, I received the call that a seat had opened up and I now had a spot. For a split second, I considered declining but I contemplated how much this meant for my parents and the years of work I put into this. My friend who was standing beside me congratulated me profusely. I was not about to let her or everyone else who believed in me down by saying "No" to this. I accepted the invitation and hustled to prepare for the first semester.

Although I liked school and liked learning, I just did not like this particular subject matter. I would have preferred human psychology to physiology, human behavior to anatomy. Even so, it came easily to me. I napped during most lectures and studied on my own while working at the medical school library. I was able to learn the material quickly, and retain information with ease. The more I studied and passed the tests, the more I convinced myself that this was where I was meant to be.

I was transforming; conforming to the role of a doctor. I started to behave differently; feel differently. I had to be professional, even in public. I worried that patients I had met in clinical rotations would see me out in public places and think less of me if I was being my loud, playful self. I felt I was now being held to a higher standard. I started to feel like I didn't fit in with my non-medical friends anymore, that we had nothing in common. I broke up with my amazing boyfriend of two years because it seemed like I was running a mile a minute, while he was still lollygagging to finish his last year of college. We no longer had anything in common.

I was troubled and torn. There was a lot of pressure to fit this image of a confident, poised doctor but this was not who I felt like on the inside. Once again, I felt restricted. In an attempt to rebel, I started hanging out with people who were completely different from my medical school colleagues. My neighbors were young musicians in a rock band, and I found myself escaping from medical school life by hanging out with them and their friends at concerts. I would stay out all night at the bar when I knew I was supposed to be studying. They had the freedom that I longed for. They could color their hair however their mood dictated and could pierce and tattoo any part of their bodies. No one scrutinized how they behaved. There was no image to live up to. When I was with them, I could pretend to be someone else.

Increasingly, I felt like I was losing myself. I was twisting and turning, snipping and cutting to fit into this mold of who I was supposed to be. Truthfully, I didn't even know who I was anymore, or who I wanted to be. But I just had to keep going; to keep pushing toward the finish line; complete medical school and residency. Then I could do whatever I wanted. I could take a teaching job or go back to research; Maybe even go back to college for that psychology degree. Ever so naïve, I didn't think about the 300,000-dollar weight of student loans that would sit on my chest stifling me until they were all paid off.

Between lectures, tests, and whatever studying I was doing, I barely had time to do any of the creative things I loved. As a child, and throughout high school and college, I had spent countless hours reading books for pleasure. During high school I sang in the choir, played in the band, acted in the drama team, and signed on the sign language team. During college, I had spent my free time painting and writing poetry. But those days were gone.

Things only worsened when I started my residency training. In addition to the studying, test taking, and attending didactic courses, I had to work 60 to 80 hours a week and also give presentations. Not only was there no time, but there was also no inspiration. I would buy new brushes and paints and stare blankly at the white canvas. Painting had been a source of relaxation but it now felt like work. I used to wake up in the middle of the night with poems swirling in my head holding me captive and alert until I would write them down; words pouring onto the paper like waterfalls. But now, I struggled to trickle out even one sentence and the words I wrote felt forced. I had all these feelings bottled up and no way to express them. I could not even enjoy reading a book for leisure. I would skim through the pages looking for the main points like I did with my medical textbooks. Just another example of me slipping away.

The final nail in the coffin was the trauma I experienced in residency, a trauma that no one ever really prepared me for. I'm not referring to the complete lack of sleep, or the constant pressure from my seniors and administrators, or the abuse from the patients I was trying to help. No, I'm talking about watching patients die.

Imagine caring for someone every day; desperately trying to find something that would work for them— anything to save them. Talking to unconscious patients on ventilators, with tubes in every body orifice, wondering if they could even hear me. Praying over their beds, futilely trying to comfort grieving family members; trying to offer hope. Pushing my hands down on their chests, feeling their ribs crack under the weight, hearing the sickening crunches. Pushing fluids and drugs, anxiously staring at the rhythm strip on the EKG monitor only to see a flat line.

The first patient of mine to die in residency was a young mother of small children. She had been in the ICU and seemed to be on her way to recovery. Unexpectedly, she rapidly declined. We tried to resuscitate her for what felt both like seconds and ages at the same time. When she died, I ran to the stairwell and sobbed, but my crying was cut short by multiple pages coming in on my beeper. I was forced to go back to work and pretend as if nothing had happened. There was no time to process, no time to release the feelings from that trauma. The more people I watched die, the more numb I became. I just went about business as usual. But was I numb? Or did I just swallow the pain without chewing, only to violently regurgitate all that undigested material when I finally got a break? I would finally have a quiet moment, maybe in the car or in the shower, and the dam would break free as rage and anguish gushed through my body.

Things were better for me outside of the hospital. I enjoyed working in the clinic and creating lasting relationships. When I started my first job with a community health center, I was ecstatic. I had my own panel of patients whom I saw regularly. I could get to know them, almost like they were extended family members. After all, I saw them more than my own family. They talked about their families, their pets, their jobs, and their travels. They shared their hopes and dreams for the future. They told me secrets they were too embarrassed or afraid to tell their own families. It was rewarding work and I truly enjoyed taking care of my patients.

Yet, there were things about it that I did not love. The administrator was not a doctor, but rather was a businessman to the core. It was all about the numbers for him. I was already seeing patients in fifteen-minute blocks while squeezing in walk-ins, but it was not enough. I was constantly being badgered by my boss to see more patients. I was pressured to write referrals to in-house specialists, even when I felt it unnecessary. He would go into tirades in my office within earshot of my patients about how I did not understand how to practice medicine. The harassment and lack of respect were both humiliating and discouraging.

I also dreaded dealing with insurance companies' issues. It was disheartening to see patients who were unable to afford medications or necessary testing and services. I tried to help by prescribing alternate affordable medications, but I always felt disappointed that I could not give them a first and usually better choice. I spent many hours of the day at work filling out lengthy prior authorization forms or calling the insurance company to get them to cover a medication or test. It was frustrating spending precious patient-facing time on that nonsense, but even more infuriating was the fact that I was limited in my ability to provide the type of care that I wanted to.

Despite my lamentations, there are things I am still grateful for. My position has given me more access to resources and knowledge to battle my disease. I am in a community of intelligent physicians of all specialties from whom I can seek advice. It has also given me the opportunity to do good and touch people's lives. I have a better understanding of what patients experience which in turn has made me a more conscientious and empathetic doctor. The lessons I have learned from my predecessors and patients are invaluable, and I will carry them for the rest of my life. Nothing can replace the unique and diverse bonds I created with my colleagues and patients through this voyage, and the love I found in my husband. Medicine may not have been what I wanted, but maybe it was just what I needed.

Chapter

9

The New Normal

When I was first diagnosed with lupus, I spent a lot of time scouring lupus websites and blogs for information. Every time I saw or heard the term "new normal", I felt dispirited. The new normal seemed like being content with living a life that was less than. The new normal sounded like giving up and giving in. The new normal looked like settling for something less.

I, however, was not ready to throw in the towel. I was going to continue living my life just as I had been doing. I was smart and had easy access to cutting edge information. I became dedicated to taking good care of myself, keeping doctors' appointments, and taking my medications faithfully. Nothing could keep me from living my "old normal" life.

And I did it. I continued working full time because I needed the money and I wanted to prove to myself that I was strong enough. I continued traveling with my boyfriend despite rational fears I had. I continued my strenuous hour-long daily workout routine, pushing myself to lose the steroid-induced weight gain. My body may have changed, but my lifestyle didn't have to.

Eventually, the stress of the job, the exercise regimen, and traveling to doctors' appointments would take their toll on me. I would end up in a flare, promise myself I would take it easy. I would get better and revert to working crazy days and over-doing my exercises. This would cause me to have another flare; usually, worse than the previous one. And so the cycle continued for years. Lather. Rinse. Repeat.

It finally got through my thick skull that this cyclical pattern wasn't working. Instead of insisting on an earned raise, I took a pay cut and went part time at thirty-two hours a week with benefits. I shortened my daily workouts to forty-five minutes. I now had a day during the week to get some rest and make it to my doctor's appointments without having to rush out of work for a late evening appointment. I was maintaining a normal life.

Once my job contract ended, I chose to stay out of work for a few months as I had started to feel burnt-out. My stress levels had been at an all-time high between working in a hostile environment, planning my wedding in another state, and trying to negotiate peace with my future in-laws. I was–genuinely considering switching gears and changing careers. I needed to do something less stressful.

When I was offered a locum tenens job in a mobile unit three days a week, I almost declined. I was not yet ready to go back to clinical medicine. I had been looking for jobs in teaching or nonclinical medicine for about three months but had not found anything. This job was going to be a three-month term in a location about ten minutes from where I lived, so I took it. It was exactly what I needed at the time.

The driver of the mobile unit was a kind, older gentleman. We had a lot of downtime on the bus and would spend our free time chatting. For nine months, he shared stories about his family and his life. We discussed my marriage and my health. We had deep, lengthy conversations about God and faith. Slowly, he helped me realize that maybe I didn't need to live the life I had before lupus. I had been afraid of the stigma and backlash I would receive for going part-time. In the medical community, there is a lot of negativity toward physicians who leave clinical medicine or go part-time, especially females. Some think it's a waste of a coveted medical school seat or residency spot. But I was not less of a person or doctor just because I worked part-time. I was still helping people, still doing good.

Working part-time was life-altering. I felt less mental and physical stress. My body was more rested and had time to recuperate. There were fewer muscle aches and joint pains. I was able to do more chores at home, which relieved my husband's stress after coming home from long days in the operating room. My husband was happier; I was happier. Our marriage flourished. I was finding more time to pray, read my Bible and do my daily devotions. Maybe a new normal was not as bad as I thought.

The "new normal" is different for everyone and it has me taken some time to accept my new normal and to understand that my new normal is constantly changing. What is normal for me this week, may not be normal for me next week and that is OK. This week I may be able to work out every day and lift ten-pound weights, next week I may only do two days while barely curling a three-pounder. I could stay up late rocking out at a concert tonight but a couple of days later be snuggled up and ready for bed by 9 p.m.

Despite my stubbornness, I have made adjustments to my lifestyle. The key has been paying attention and listening to my body. I take a nap every day, even if it is just lying down and resting my mind for twenty minutes. I exercise every weekday but allow myself a break on the weekends and I don't push myself if I am not feeling well. I have decided on a three-day work week maximum in order to maintain my sanity and my physical health. I have also made a conscious effort to cut out inflammatory foods from my diet. Although, I admit this still a struggle since I love all things sweet or fried. When we take vacations, we plan for half-day activities and leave time to relax. I have accepted that there will be bad days where my to-do list will have to wait and all I will be able to do is sleep. I take advantage of the good days instead of procrastinating.

The most important lesson I have learned in my journey to find my new normal is to focus on what I can do, instead of what I cannot do. My life has not been limited; it has just evolved. There may be roadblocks and barriers in my path, and I may not be able to climb over them; however, I can always find a way around them. I'm still cautious, but I try not to let fear dictate my life anymore. I believe, with faith, I can overcome anything. In my new normal there will be struggles, but also opportunities that I never imagined. Every day is a new surprise, and I am here for it!

Speaking of Surprises ...

I'm having a baby!!!

10

Doctor's Orders (Tips for living with chronic disease)

Preparing for Doctors' Visits

1. Write down all medications you take, including doses AND recommended times. A lot of doctors even request that you bring in the medication bottles. I have checked prescription bottles myself and caught a few errors where some of my patients were still taking a previous prescription dose or they had two bottles of the same medication (generic and brand) prescribed by different physicians.

2. Write down your list of questions before you go, so you don't forget when you are caught up in the visit. I find there is so much going on in such a short time, that unless I have my questions written down, I miss something.

3. Make a daily diary or log of symptoms and review it before the appointment. You might have noticed a new symptom a few weeks before the appointment and may forget to bring it up.

4. Take pictures. For symptoms such as rash, pictures serve as documentation in case the rash resolves, and also allows the doctor to see the progression of the rash.

5. Bring all test results or consults from other doctors to your current appointment. In a perfect world, all the information should transfer between doctors' offices in time for the appointment, but this does not always happen.

6. Dress comfortably and bring something to do while waiting. It makes the waiting time more tolerable and reduces anxiety.

7. Bring a notepad and pen to take notes.

8. If you feel comfortable, bring a friend or family member for moral support and an extra pair of ears.

Talking to Your Doctor

1. Engage in the conversation. Be assertive. This is YOUR appointment.

2. Be careful not to bias the doctor. A lot of times we are so convinced that we have a certain condition, that we inadvertently fail to tell the whole story, and tell only what fits the picture of what we think we have, leaving out important details.

3. Describe symptoms in terms of functionality. For example instead of saying "My pain is so bad", say " I am in so much pain, I cannot sit up or get out of bed". Help the doctor understand any limitations your symptoms might be causing you.

4. Don't be afraid to ask for further explanation or for something to be repeated if you don't understand. There is no such thing as a stupid question when it comes to your health.

5. Summarize your plan at the end of the visit to ensure there is no misunderstanding. For example,

you can say "Ok doctor. You want me to stop medication X. You are ordering bloodwork for me to do one week before my next visit and you want to see me back in 4 weeks."

Taking Control of Your Healthcare

1. If you are not comfortable with your doctor or with their recommendations, get a second opinion. The doctor-patient relationship is sacred, and you need to be able to trust the person taking care of you.

2. Do not be afraid to call or message the doctor if something doesn't feel right. That's why doctors are on call.

3. Be organized. Keep track of your medical appointments and note when all your drug refills are due rather than depend on the doctor's office or the pharmacy for reminders. From my experience, specialty medications are not always stocked at pharmacies and may need to be ordered in advance.

4. Educate yourself about the disease and ways to manage it. There are a ton of books, and oodles of information on the internet. Just make sure to consult reliable sources.

5. Research resources such as prescription assistance programs, patient care programs and other benefits that may be offered by your insurance company. There's no way I would have been able to afford my Benlysta® without co-pay assistance. Check your medication's manufacturer website or your insurance company for resources and benefits

Maintaining Relationships

1. Teach the people in your life about your disease and how it affects you. Your disease is part of you now and it's important for them to know and understand that part of you. If you have trouble explaining, or if they want more information, you can always refer them to an official website about your disease. Many such websites are maintained by non-profit organizations focused on specific diseases.

2. Use social apps such as Facetime or Houseparty to "hang out" with friends when you don't feel up to going out. My family lives far from me but we love being able to talk and play an online game together.

3. Be spontaneous and take advantage of good days. I love planning, but sometimes I just can't make plans because I'm not feeling well. I find that those last-minute get-togethers end up being my most favorite outings.

4. Join a support group and make new friends! Online communities are great for this.

5. For couples, counseling can be an invaluable resource. Being sick or being the caregiver for a sick partner can be stressful and create tension in a relationship. Having the chance to talk to someone who is unbiased and work out ways to cope is priceless.

6. Remember that our friends and family need support too. Sometimes we get so caught up in our own suffering that we ignore the problems of the ones we love. As Ralph Waldo Emerson quoted "The only way to have a friend is to be one."

7. Step away from unsupportive relationships. If someone is unwilling to understand, they are not worth the relational stress.

8. Learn to forgive. Not everyone is going to be understanding or kind but holding on to resentment hurts you more than it does them.

Notes For Caregivers

1. Be patient. With the ones you are caring for and with yourself. It's a learning curve for everyone.

2. Communicate. It is so important to communicate with each other—your feelings, needs, and expectations. This way everyone is always on the same page.

3. Educate yourself about the illness that the person you are caring for has. There are lots of resources online. It may also be helpful to attend doctor's appointments with them or join them in their support groups (with their consent).

4. Respect the patient's need for independence. It is easy when caring for someone to get into the habit of doing everything for them, especially with older people. Allow them to do the things they want to and are able to do.

5. Make time to care for yourself. This is something I tell my patients who are also caregivers. It is like when you are on an airplane and they tell you to put on your oxygen mask first before helping your child. You can't help someone else if you are not well.

6. Ask for help. Sometimes it can be overwhelming caring for someone who is sick. It's OK to take a break or ask another friend or family member to help with some of the duties.

7. Most importantly, listen to the patient, believe what they are saying, and acknowledge their feelings.

Plan for Emergencies

1. Carry a list of medications and emergency contacts (including doctors) with you in your wallet or purse.

2. Have a back-up plan for someone to pick up your children and care for your pets (if you have them).

3. If possible, squirrel away a little money every month in an emergency fund. Getting sick can mean extra medical bills and missed days from work, so it's good to have money saved for times like these.

4. Make sure you have all medical/legal paperwork in order such as a health care proxy and a DNR (Do Not Resuscitate) status.

Practice Self-care

1. Schedule your rest time. I am a "nap-aholic" and I say that unashamedly. Even on the busiest of days, I try to squeeze in twenty minutes of quiet time to lie down and rest my body.

2. Exercise. It doesn't have to be strenuous. Walking, at a mild to moderate pace, is beneficial. For me exercise boosts both my energy levels and my mood. I love to vary my workouts from cardio, weight-training, and yoga so that I can get the benefits of weight loss, stamina, strength, and flexibility. Find something that works for you and make it a routine.

3. Eat a healthy diet tailored to you. There are multitudes of online resources and books to help with a specific diet for your condition. It also helps to speak with a certified dietician.

4. Do things you enjoy. Be positive and focus on the things you can do. Do not be afraid to try something new.

5. Learn to say no. You do not have to do everything everyone asks you or attend everyone's event. They will get over it.

6. Surround yourself with people who love you. Having a strong support system has been crucial to my well-being.

7. Get some fresh air. Sometimes sitting outside for a few minutes is all I need to brighten my mood.

8. Pray or meditate daily. My morning devotions are what set the tone for the rest of my day, and praying throughout the day keeps me on track.

9. Talk to a therapist or life coach. We are dealing with so much on a daily basis, it is beneficial to have someone to talk to who can help us work through feelings. Journaling is also another great for tool for expressing our feelings.

10. Most importantly, be positive. A quote by one of my favorite authors, Charles R Swindoll, comes to mind: "Life is 10 percent what happens to you, and 90 percent how you react to it". We can't change the fact that we live with a chronic illness, but we can change how we live with that chronic illness.

CONTACT INFORMATION

You can contact Dr. Rayavarapu at:

mail@thepatientdoc.com

Facebook: www.facebook.com/manisharayavarapu

Instagram:@manisharayavarapu

www.thepatientdoc.com

Made in the USA
Las Vegas, NV
14 March 2024

87182152R00066